Transforming

Illness

To

Wellness

Two Weeks to
Transform YOUR LIFE!

Carol L Rickard, LCSW

Well YOUniversity® Publications

ISBN-13: 978-0-9821010-2-5

Transforming Illness to Wellness

by Carol L Rickard, LCSW

Well YOUniversity, LLC

5 Zion Road, Hopewell, NJ 08525

www.WellYOUniversity.com

888 LifeTools

What you will get out of this book?!

- ✓ A proven system for creating healthy changes in your life.

- ✓ Being better able to **manage your life** rather than *illness* managing it for you!

- ✓ A way of tracking and measuring your wellness foundation.

- ✓ Improved quality of life!

Contents

The L.I.F.E. Wellness Blueprint:

Building the Foundation Corners!

Building the Rest of the Foundation!

Introduction

For over **20** years I've been working in
hospital programs helping **1,000's**
of people reclaim their lives from illness.

The biggest misconception many people have is:

You **can't** have wellness
IF you *have an illness.*

This is so not true!

I will share a **wonderful** definition of wellness.
This definition is the foundation of *all* the work I do.

It is also the foundation for my own life!

It also seems that once a person is

diagnosed with a chronic illness,

they tend to *resign themselves*

to a life ***without*** wellness.

It's as if they feel they *don't*

have control anymore

&

end up *taking their hands*

off the 'steering wheel of life'.

In the next chapter,

we will look at *WHY*

you need to put your hands

back on the steering wheel!

Touched by Illness

My life has been touched by illness as **both**

the patient and the family member.

My earliest experience with illness taking over

goes all the way back to my

My father had cancer & died
my freshman year in high school.

My mother ended up getting

VERY SICK just after that.

She actually had been given *'last rights'* twice.

Since my younger brother was at home –
I became the person responsible for many things.

The roles between child & parent became reversed.

This included:

~ learning to drive **2 years** before legal age!

~ doing the  , cooking, &

~ making sure she **took her medications**
& got to her doctor's appointment.

I basically did most of the things
my mother *would have done*
had she only ***been able to.***

And so,

It's not just one person's life that's impacted
when illness takes over –
it's the ***entire family's.***

This makes it even more important
to create some wellness in your life.

My life was again touched by illness
after my mother had passed away.....

this time as the patient.

My health had slowly been going

I was seeing my primary care doctor
every few of months & getting

tested for this & for that.

At the same time,

symptoms started to slowly take over my life......

It got to the point I could barely
get back & forth to work every day.

There were even a few days where
I **walked in** to work **only** to
turn around to leave & *go back home.*

Fortunately, I had a supportive supervisor….

(I know others are not always so fortunate)

It felt like things had to
totally hit bottom in order for me
to begin a journey back to wellness.

My purpose in writing this book is that –

1) YOU don't have to 'hit bottom' in order to get well.

2) YOU have **a way** to *get out* if that's where you are.

I honestly believe this is what
God *had in mind for me* putting me
to work in that hospital 23 years ago:

* Learning how to get myself well 1st!

* Helping others how to do the same!

About This Book

In my years of helping people successfully change health habits, I've reached a conclusion I would like to share with you:

I believe people are *already smart enough* when it comes to being healthy.

You **KNOW WHAT TO DO!**

It's the '*DOING*' or *lack of it* that keeps you stuck where you are.

I can help *change* that!

I doubt you have read a 📖 like this! Unless, of course, you may have read any of my **5** other books!

Along with **simple** & easy to understand chapters,

I tend to use a lot of pictures,

analogies

& word art

to make the information stick in the brain!

I like to describe this approach as:

Whole Brain Health

It's what makes my books and services

different from all others!

KNOWLEDGE is the left brain at work.

This is where YOU *know* what to do!

Because I use "pictures" & "images", I end up

tapping in to the other side of the brain –

the right side!

This is also the side that synthesizes things,

like the operating system in a computer!

With both sides working on the 'same page',
the end result is getting people to

Move knowledge in to ACTION!

This book will introduce you to
a *proven system* for taking back

CONTROL of your L.I.F.E.

Up until NOW,
in order to get these 'insider secrets,
you'd have to get sick enough to
end up at the hospital.

That's WHY I am so excited

to be sharing them with you in this book!

Patients used to look at me like
I had a 3rd eye every time I said
they were *"lucky to end up in the hospital."*

Then I'd clarify –

I didn't mean lucky to get sick….

"**Lucky** to be learning skills *EVERYONE needs*
to learn yet won't have the chance!

Today, YOU get an

opportunity to learn for yourself!

What this *won't do:*

It ***WILL NOT*** give you 'the cure' to any illness.

It ***WILL NOT*** get any illness to 'go away'.

It ***WILL NOT*** give you 'a quick fix'.

It ***WILL NOT*** *even* give you 'a fix'.

It will give you back
a foundation for your life.

This foundation will give you the base that you
need in order to be *living well* with an illness!

So let's get moving on to the

L.I.F.E. Wellness Blueprint

Here is my wordtool for life:

Living

Intentionally &

Fully

Engaged

Taken from "Words at Work"

IT'S NOT

WHAT HAPPENS **TO YOU**

BUT

HOW **YOU REACT** *TO IT*

THAT MATTERS

EPICTETUS

Getting Started!

Two birds are sitting on a wire.

One decides to fly away.

How many are left?

I like to start off my live workshops

with this little riddle.

It had such a tremendous impact on my life

the first time I heard it!

When they asked us to raise our hand

If we thought the answer was **one** -

My hand went up high & proud!

Wrong! The answer is two.

Oops!

DECIDING & DOING

are two different things!

Just because you decide to do something

DOESN'T mean that you DO it!

Now, I don't know about you –

But there had been plenty of times

In my life when I **Decided**

&

I *NEVER* FOLLOWED THRU!

(This little riddle *helped change that!)*

This is my wordtool to get moving!

Direct

Opportunity

The same rule applies to this

If you don't use it, it *won't work*.

KNOWING & DOING

are two different things!

We either:

 **opportunity**

or

IT gets *directed for us!*

And chances are we WON'T like

the direction we get taken!

? For YOU: **?**

Isn't it time you start steering

your LIFE in **a new direction***?*

I know how easy it is to get LOST…..

23 years ago

when my life was taken over by symptoms….

Every aspect of my life was impacted…..

work, family, friends, hobbies, relationships.

It doesn't have to STAY this way.

DECIDE *right here, right now*

You're going to put your hands on the wheel

& take back the direction of

I promise to help you

DO IT!

What I say to everyone:

(including myself!)

YOU *ARE NOT* RESPONSIBLE FOR YOUR ILLNESS,

YOU **MUST TAKE** *RESPONSIBILITY* FOR YOUR WELLNESS.

CAROL L RICKARD

What is Wellness?

What is Wellness?

For many years, I used to define wellness as

"optimal health".

I liked the definition because <u>not</u> <u>everyone's</u> the same.

No illness is the same.

What is optimal for my girlfriend with

Lupus is not the same as my brother's CLL.

Some years ago, as I was preparing

for a speech, I came across the

BEST definition.

I love to share it with others!

<u>The National Wellness Institute's:</u>

"Wellness is an *active process* of *becoming*

aware of & *making choices* towards

a *MORE* successful existence."

I'd like to break this down &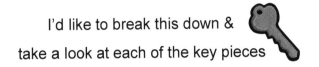
take a look at each of the key pieces

active process

WE must take some kind of action.

WELLNESS *doesn't happen* by ACCIDENT!

This means you & I must take responsibility

& DO STUFF!

One of the secrets I've learned over the past 23

years is *even a little action works!*

HAVE you ever saved pennies, nickels,

dimes, & quarters? Then you know!

They seem like such small amounts –

especially the pennies nickels & dimes!

Yet, they can ADD UP!

We'll talk about 'making changes' in a later chapter.
I have some secrets to share with you!

Here is my wordtool for action:

A
Critical
Task
Implemented
Only
Now!

© 2015 & licensed by Well YOUniversity, LLC
Taken from "Words at Work"

<u>becoming aware of</u>

What you're doing at this very moment,
just by reading this book!

By keeping an open ear & an open mind
you have taken the 1st step.

When we say:

"That won't work for me."

"That has nothing to do with me."

"How could that possibly work?"

We are not keeping an open mind….

Be on the lookout

Don't let your mind sneak shut on you
AT ANY TIME!

You don't have to **AGREE with everything.**

You DO have to **BE OPEN to everything!**

One other critical step is to start

becoming aware of your behaviors.

Are there things you are currently either

DOING or NOT DOING

that are keeping you stuck?

This means taking an honest look at WHAT

you're doing & answering the following:

   OR

Here is my wordtool for action:

$$A\text{ctively}$$

$$W\text{ork}$$

$$A\text{t}$$

$$R\text{ecognizing}$$

$$E\text{xistence}$$

making choices

NOBODY chooses to get sick or have an illness.

And yet, we *must choose to get well.*

The choices we make TODAY make
a difference in moving us towards either:

Illness ^{or} **Wellness**

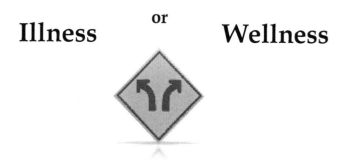

Many times it *may seem like*

we **don't even** have a choice.....

This can happen when we don't like any
of the options we have to choose from.

Don't be fooled by this!

Just because we *may not like the options,*
Doesn't mean that we shouldn't choose!

In fact, this may be the most critical time to
exercise our power to choose

Of all of God's creatures on earth –

we humans are the only ones who

have this power! WE MUST USE IT

Here is my wordtool for choice:

Controlling

How

Our

Intentions

Create

Experiences

© 2015 & licensed by Well YOUniversity, LLC
Taken from "Words at Work"

I wanted to share with you one of the most
POWERFUL quotes I have ever heard:

WHEN WE FACE A SITUATION

THAT *CANNOT* BE CHANGED

WE ARE CHALLENGED

TO **CHANGE OURSELVES**

VICTOR FRANKL

Dr. Victor Frankl survived 3 years in concentration
camps. If you have not read his book, I would highly
recommend it; *Man's Search For Meaning*

<u>more successful existence</u>

I LOVE that *this applies to EVERYONE!*

So if the symptoms never go away completely,

Or

The illness just gets worse over time -

a person can always

AIM to have a

"successful existence"

And most importantly,

What that is for one person

doesn't mean

it has to be for EVERYONE.

This definition provides the HOPE that we can have

illness & wellness at the SAME TIME!

The Blueprint

#1) What It Is! What It Is Not!

What It Is!

LIFE Wellness Blueprint™ is a structured system
that helps people rebuild & reclaim
their lives from illness

As you will see, we **need** to do more
than just take medications…….

Medication is *ONLY* **1 tool!** There are many more!

My promise is simple:

Follow this blueprint for the next 2 weeks,
And you'll definitely see a difference in your life

Just as with any type of blueprint-

When we follow it …..
we end up with the same results
every time! In this case –

It's **QUALITY OF LIFE!**

What It Is Not!

The Blueprint is **NOT** a replacement for treatment with a professional healthcare provider.

Anybody using this book also needs to be connected to some type of **healthcare professional:**

For treatment of their health needs.

After all, the next important thing to having a blueprint to follow --

Is having a responsible

BUILDING CONTRACTOR

supervise the work!!

2) Taking A Look at the Blueprint

I need you to imagine…

I am standing on this 4-legged chair right in front of you!

You saw off one of the legs….

What do you think will happen?   *Do I fall on you?!*

Probably not –

since I have 3 legs I can still shift my weight to!

After all,

 A stool only has 3 legs!

I'll bet you have probably sat on one of these!

The problem with stools is that they aren't too sturdy!

I have sat on a 3-legged stool

AND I have tipped over on one....

You come along & saw off another leg!

What happens to me now?!

34

The truth is …….

I could only stay up on those things for a short time!

Even if I was good at stilts -

it wouldn't take *much of a bump to knock me over.*

(We all know *LIFE IS FULL OF BUMPS*!).

Now, you saw off the 3rd leg -

Leaving me with only 1!!!!

What do you think is going to happen to me?

You're right!   *I'm going down…*

Oops!

I never could pogo stick!

So, when we expect just

the medication

to make us well…..

IT CAN"T – IT IS ONLY 1 LEG!

L.I.F.E. WELLNESS

M
E
D
I
C
A
T
I
O
N

(Pretty wobbly!)

As you can see, this is what

the blueprint would

look like with just medication…..

At the same time,

I've worked with many people

who kept trying to get well

WITHOUT MEDICATION –

When you need it – YOU NEED IT!

This won't get you well either!

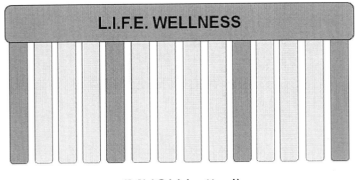

(MUCH better!)

This is what the complete blueprint
looks like at the end of 2 weeks!

Now, I want you to imagine
me standing on this chair with **14** legs…

Don't you agree that would give me a

"**solid**, "**strong**", "**stable**", "**sturdy**" foundation?!!

This is exactly how you will find

your *L.I.F.E. foundation*

when you build out this blueprint!

The reason we need to have such a solid

foundation is because of this *thing* called

I like to think & teach that

stress is *like an earthquake*!

It can really shake up our lives!

 Foundations tend to take

a bruising during earthquakes

& parts have been known to fall down.

We've got to make sure

WE HAVE PLENTY of foundation!

When we **START** to *lose some of it*

to a big stressor going on in our lives

or

even a *WHOLE BUNCH* of little stressors -

39

We've got to have enough left

to keep us **standing!**

Lost some!

**Still have
enough left!**

It could even be that

the **STRESS** of your illness

has *taken down* what you had in place

as your **existing foundation**

In which case, you're in the REBUILDING stage!

The Domino Effect

Now,

it's important to understand how this foundation can

CRUMBLE!

under certain circumstances

&

lead to the illness **taking over again**...

If you lose one of the **4** foundation corners......

it sets off a '*domino effect*' and the others start to fall.

You might be able to go weeks or months

BUT the illness can start to take over again.....

Which is why *it's important* to adopt the

 approach as **a way of *LIVING***

rather than as a *short term solution!*

Building the

Foundation Corners

Day 1 - Medication

This can sometimes be one of the

hardest & most frustrating parts

to get right depending on the illness you have.

That's why it's important

to keep **many** of the other parts in place!

This is also **a very personal area.**

There are *many people* who don't
believe in the use of any medications…

or prefer to use a holistic approach.

It's important for me to respect people's beliefs.

If this is you,

it means you would use whatever is your holistic

approach in place of the medication.

If you were someone who is

not using any medications

you might want to skip past the transformation tips

&

move on to Day 2

44

When it comes to **Medication**

Here are some

Transformation Tips!

To STAY where you are:

✓   Miss doses & don't tell your prescriber.

✓   Run out of medication all together!

✓   Stop taking them!

People can **feel better** & *don't think they need them*

or

still feel bad & **don't think they are working!**

❖   Drink alcohol -

 even a couple glasses of wine can be too much of a mix with medications.

❖   Start changing the amounts on your own!

Most important to moving forward:

1. **Don't let other people** *decide for you.*

2. Take all medication as **prescribed!**

3. *Talk* with your prescriber and *be honest* if you have missed doses or stopped taking.

4. Discuss any **EFFECTS** or **CONCERNS**

5. If you have limited finances or no insurance, make sure this is shared with your provider.

6. Do not put M.D. after your name.
    Let your prescriber make the changes!

7. If you **HATE** taking medications but **know you need to keep taking them** - *SAY THIS* when you take them:

	or	
I *hate* taking these treatments, but I *know I need them.*		I *hate* taking these medications, but I *know I need them.*

There are also some strategies I came up with to help me **REMEMBER** *my dog's medication* – she has seizures & takes 4 different ones!

Kalley

- ❖ DUAL alarm clock in my kitchen – this way I hear it *wherever I am in the house!*

- ❖ 2 pill boxes at a time – this way I know ahead of time when I am running low on meds!

- ❖ Link it - The food doesn't go in her mouth until the pills do first!

- ❖ Schedule it – I write in in my planner every day at the times she's due!

- ❖ Changed the Times – Asked the vet if we could take the one at earlier time!

SPECIAL NOTICE:

It is critical that you SHOP AROUND for

the *cheapest* place to buy your medications!

 NOT ALL PHARMACIES
ARE THE SAME...

I once helped a patient who had

a **%** copay on her medications.

We checked the price of a 30-day supply:

Pharmacy A – $ 1,156.00

Pharmacy B – $ 968.00

Pharmacy C – $ 823.00

Pharmacy D – $ 688.00

I buy Kalley's meds at **COSTCO**
(*you don't have to be a member for medicine*)

Costco - 1 month supply = $ 39.50

Other membership store = $ 202.50

* they offered to match but I couldn't in good faith knowing
if *you* didn't know that – you'd pay full price

Day 2 – Structure

Since this is one of the corners of the foundation-

it can *make or break* your recovery.

One good way to think about structure is:

"What routines do you follow?"

Another good way to think about it is

"What do you do with *your time?*"

For a lot of people, structure is created

by **work, school, family obligations**.

For many people, an illness can completely

DESTROY *what structure* they had in place.

What happens when that changes?

My experience has been that once a person is unable to do the things they'd **normally do** to create structure in their day......

They get a lot sicker

This is particular the case with

WORK

It seemed that **while a person was working**, *they were better able* to manage the illness.

Once they lost work,

The **balance tipped** in the direction of the illness

Maybe you're someone who

doesn't have much structure to start with

OR

One of those who has

TOO MUCH to do & *too little time*?

Then *all the more reason* you will need

to **concentrate** on this area!

I created a tool for my patients I call

LIFE Daily Wellness Plan

I use it every day!

I've made a short video you
can watch at:

WellYOUniversity.com/Plan

You'll also be able to
download a copy
of the planner!

Structure is **critical** to stability. It's really 2 steps:

1. Having a daily structure in place

2. Making sure it is balanced

When it comes to **Structure**

Here are some

Transformation Tips!

To stay where you are:

✓ Wake up when you want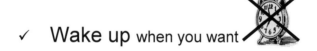

✓ **Don't** have **any plan or structure** to your day.

✓ Have **too much free time**

on your hands.

✓ Try to **take on** *too many* things in the day

✓ Stay in bed or in
   the bedroom all day.

✓ Watch **TV** 12 hours a day......

Most important to moving forward!

1. Set the alarm & wake up at a consistent time
   (*No longer* than 1 extra hour on weekends!)

2. Have a **daily schedule** written out & follow it!

3. If you are *not working*, make sure to fill the daily
   plan with other activities – **volunteer!**

4. If a parent, create some 'me' time -
   even if it's just five minutes.

5. Limit the television you watch.

6. Get outside for 15 minutes.

7. DO NOT *isolate* yourself in one room.

8. Make sure you have the **other parts** of the **Blueprint** planned in your day.

9. Use an appointment book
   or calendar

10. Work on household chores even if for only **5** minutes at a time!

11. USE the LIFE Daily Planner every day!

Day 3 – Healthcare F/U

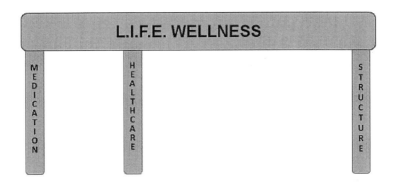

Staying current and *up to date* with all of your healthcare needs is important.

When you are someone living with a chronic illness or health issue, this is *EVEN MORE IMPORTANT.*

HOW MANY CARS HAVE YOU OWNED?

or

HOW MANY HAVE BEEN IN YOUR HOUSEHOLD?
(This includes new & used ones!)

1   **5**

3

Maybe More!
(Depending on your age of course!)

Imagine....

You had 1 car that had to last you a lifetime.

How well would you take care of that car?!

If you are like most people,

you would probably take very good care of it,

including regular *preventive* maintenance!

Well, I love to be the one to break the news to you...

We **ONLY** get one vehicle to *live our life with!*

ONE BODY that has to
LAST A LIFETIME!

It was my chiropractor who had this
up on his board one day!

I had been taking pretty good care of myself,
However, when I saw this *I realized*

I could be doing a little better!

Imagine you had a new car that had
to be taken in regularly for it's

30,000
&
60,000

mile tune-ups.

You wouldn't just blow it off, **right?**

Even those of us *living with an illness*

still need to keep up with

the other parts of car!

So don't just **limit you focus & attention** on the

1 part that needs monitoring -

You've got to keep an eye

out on **the WHOLE vehicle!**

This way we can work to try &

avoid other parts breaking down.

Another important piece to be *aware of*

&

which has to do with our healthcare is:

WHO we are seeing as a provider!

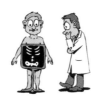

Because resources are often so limited –

many people end up having their illness
be managed by their **Primary Care doctor**

 OR

by a local health clinic.

If you are in this type of situation

&

feel your symptoms

are not *stabilizing or improving -*

ASK for a referral to a specialist.

Even clinics have doctors who **SPECIALIZE**

in treating & managing a specific illness.

You won't gain access until you ASK!

Here's why: Suppose you had a ***Porsche*** &

it needed some engine work

WHO WOULD YOU TAKE IT TO?

The Porsche Mechanic

or

The Ford Mechanic?

Most likely you said **Porsche!**

WHY?

Even though they both know
how to work on engines!

Porsche **is** their <u>area of expertise!</u>

The same holds true when it comes to *health*:

Even though primary care doctors know medicine,

A specialist has their <u>**area of expertise**</u>!
This area is ALL that they focus on -

Does that make sense?

When it comes to **Healthcare F/U**

Here are some

Transformation Tips!

To STAY where you are:

✓ *Don't even* seek help in the **1st** place.

✓ **Miss** appointments or routine check-ups.

✓ *Don't follow through* on recommended lab work or procedures.

✓ Don't communicate openly and honestly

✓ Cancel & *don't reschedule* a new appointment

✓ Drop out of treatment.

✓ Stay in treatment you *don't think is working* but **don't talk** to anyone about it.

✓ Avoid ALL healthcare providers!

Most important to moving forward

1. Make *all appointments* -
   (Whether you feel like it or not!)

2. Be **open & honest** in communications with your healthcare provider.

3. If you must cancel an appointment, make sure you *reschedule right way.*

4. **Talk** about your idea to stop treatment.

5. Let your provider know if you feel like what you doing is ***NOT*** working for you!

6. Ask to be referred to a specialist

7. Stay up to date on **ALL** preventative
   screenings

8. Remember: Treatment may take some time.

Don't give up!!!

Day 4 – Sober

Right away most people think:

"This doesn't have anything to do with me!

I don't have a problem

with drinking or using any drugs"

How I use the term – it applies to everyone!

It simply means:

Stopping

ANY

Harmful

Behaviors

What could some of these harmful behaviors be?

Are you *EATING* things you are **NOT** supposed to?

Sweets

Fried

Salty

Are you *AVOIDING* things you're supposed to **DO**?

Exercise

Meds / Treatment

Use assistance

Are you *DOING* things you **SHOULDN'T BE?**

Smoking

Working too much

Taking extra meds

Emotional Eating

Abusing alcohol / drugs

And if YOU DON'T have

any harmful behaviors...

It makes your workload a little lighter!

BEWARE!

Every time YOU engage in the harmful behavior....

You **LOSE** a corner of your **FOUNDATION**

Building the

Rest of the Foundation

Day 5 – Nutrition

There are 2 types of nutrients our bodies need which tend to get very affected by illness:

Food & *Sleep*

When it comes to *Food* –

Illness can take our eating behaviors

in the opposite directions-

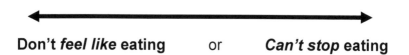

Don't *feel like* eating   or   ***Can't stop* eating**

Neither one of these will help us get better!

An important consideration is if you take medications that *increase cravings for sweets* –

This CAN LEAD to more junk food!!

BEWARE!

It's not *just medications* that put the weight on;

it's *what we put in our mouths too!*

If you notice:

You're eating healthy, exercising,

& *still gaining weight* –

talk to your prescriber about the issue.

 ** A good prescriber **will be** concerned re: weight gain.

The other nutrient our bodies need is **sleep!**

When it comes to ***Sleep*** –

Illness can also impact our sleeping patterns.

in the opposite directions-

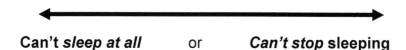

Can't *sleep at all*   or   ***Can't stop* sleeping**

Not sleeping can have such an immediate impact on *our well-being,*

This can often be what leads people to **self medicating** with drugs or alcohol.

Too much sleep can also have an impact as it starts to interfere with our daily activities.

If you must sleep during 'off hours'

try a power nap!

When it comes to **Nutrition**

Here are some

Transformation Tips!

To stay where you are:

✓ Keep *self medicating* to go to sleep.

✓ Eat based on how you feel ---

    If you're **hungry – eat**!

    If you're **not hungry – don't eat**!

✓ Drink as much caffeine as you can!

junk food

✓ Eat ALL the you like.

✓ *Don't* **talk** to your prescriber about your sleep problems.

✓ Keep sleeping as <u>much as you feel like.</u>

✓ *Take long naps* day after not sleeping well!

Most important to moving forward!

1. Talk to a health care provider about your sleep problems.

2. Manage your diet to **3** meals a day.

3. **Eat** a little bit – even if you're **not hungry**.

4. **Limit** the caffeine and junk food!

5. **STOP** self-medicating for sleep.

6. *Do not* **sleep** during the day after a night you can't sleep.

7. Do not sleep longer than **8-10 hours;** make yourself get out of bed.

8. If you **wake up at night** &

     **cannot fall back asleep,**

    GO SIT in another room until you feel tired.

    DO NOT: Smoke, clean house, or be active!

9. If your mind won't shut off,

    try **journaling**

    or

    relaxation techniques

Day 6 – Exercise

Another good way to think about exercise is think

Activity!

Exercise doesn't have to be *just* going to a gym

or doing **aerobics**

or **Weights**

or **Running**

Here it's about

increasing our *level of activity!!*

There are plenty of ways to do this

without too much inconvenience!!

Now – if you are limited in what you can do –

DO WHAT YOU CAN! Don't overdo it…

Even if it doesn't seem like much every little bit counts!

When it comes to **Exercise**

Here are some

Transformation Tips!

To stay where you are:

✓ **STOP** exercise routines completely

✓ Park your car at the *closest spot* possible!

✓ Have someone else do
   your shopping & chores

✓ Stay a couch or bed potato!

Most important to moving forward!

1) When watching TV,

   pick your feet up & down during commercials!
   (gradually build you're way up in time.)

2) Do some *extra* housecleaning = ↑
   ACTIVITY!

3) Take the elevators up but the stairs   D
                                            O
                                             W
                                              N

4) WALK to your mailbox a couple of times a day!

5) Take the dog for a walk

6) Park ⟶ f u r t h e r a w a y!

7) **Walk in-place** during TV commercials!

8) Stand up for **5** minutes every hour

9) Look for ways to get yourself moving more!

Day 7 – Support

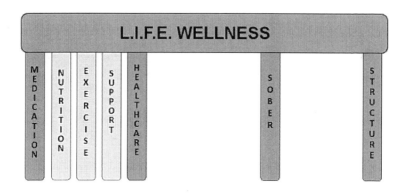

This is such an important area.

It can have a significant impact on our health –

Both positive & negative

One of the ways I help people understand the impact

of **not having support** is the following:

Parlez Vous Francaise?

Have you ever been around a group of people who

were speaking in another language you didn't

understand *AT ALL?*

How did you *feel?* What were you *thinking?*

I had this experience on a trip to see my brother, who, thanks to the Navy, was stationed in Italy.

I felt VERY anxious!

What would I do if I got lost or separated?

How would I be able to ask for help?

What were they saying about me?

The point is *people who experience illness* also speak a different language.

Not being around people
who can speak & understand it,
can leave *you* feeling **alone**,
helpless, & powerless.

Sometimes, family members are able to understand the language.

More times than not, they just are *not able* to but not for lack of wanting to!!

It's hard to speak a language if you don't know it?! And it may take them a little time to learn it!!!

When it comes to **Support**

Here are some

Transformation Tips!

To stay where you are:

✓ **DON'T** have anyone around you who can understand what *you're going thru.*

✓ Stay connected to toxic people.

✓ Listen to people who say "**get over it**" or "**stop taking the medication**".

✓ BELIEVE you are THE ONLY ONE with this.

✓ Have **no supports** at all!

Most important to moving forward!

✓ Let family and friends KNOW when they say things that *don't feel supportive.*

✓ If there is no support group available at your treatment provider, START ONE!

✓ Join in online forums and groups.

✓ If possible, have some *family counseling* with a therapist or at your church.

✓ HELP **educate others** so they
better *understand about your illness.*

✓ if your **local hospital** has any
support groups you can get involved with.

✓ Get some **counseling** for YOU!

Day 8 – Socialization

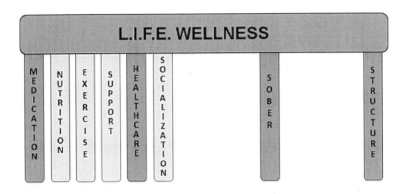

The opposite of socialization is ISOLATION!

This is the key thing we need to address.

Isolation is to an illness what a gasoline is to a fire –

 an accelerant!

Isolation has a way of *fueling* the illness,

making it even worse….

Also, be on the lookout for depression…

An *early signal* can be when you start

WITHDRAW from people you're close to.

Now, I'm not saying we have to become

a social butterfly!

But we do have to take steps & actions

to make sure we are not isolating.

When it comes to **Socialization**

Here are some

Transformation Tips!

To stay where you are:

✓   Continue avoiding **family & friends**

✓   Keep yourself hidden away in your home.

✓   Turn off your phone.

✓   Pull down all the shades & HIDE

✓ DON'T return messages, texts or emails.

✓ Avoid the mailbox and computer.

✓ Stop going to social types of gathering

✓ Stay isolated in one room.

✓ STOP going to religious services.

Most important to getting well!

1. Start spending small amounts of TIME
   outside the room you were isolated in.

2. Turn the phone back on
   & answer it!

3. ✓ the mail everyday,
   EMAIL too if you have it.

4. Make a point to **reach out to** at least 1 person.

5. Send a letter, card or
   email to someone.

6. Go spend time at the library

7. At least go to a *social function* –

   leave early if you must.

8. Talk with someone from your religious
   Organization

9.  Call a helpline.

10. Say hello to **at least** **1** **person a day!**

11. STOP ISOLATING! ~~Isolating~~

12. Send a text or leave a voice mail
    when you know no one's home!

Day 9 – LifeTools

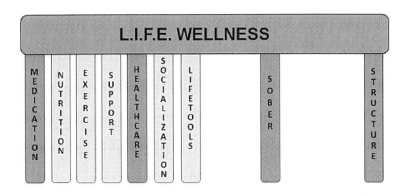

I believe there are **2** types of coping skills:

"Survival tools" & "LifeTools".

Survival tools refer to the coping skills

we tend to develop *out of the necessity*

to deal with a problem or issue in our lives.

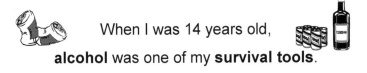

When I was 14 years old,

alcohol was one of my **survival tools**.

It's how I found to cope with overhearing & figuring out

my father was dying from CANCER

The problem with **Survival tools**:

They can become a **problem** *themselves!*

What once may have helped us *cope,*

can turn around and *start* to hurt us.

Which brings me to the **LifeTools!**

These are the **healthy** coping skills

we must DEVELOP

to **replace** the old *survival tools!*

Fortunately, I was able to **replace**

my survival tool, alcohol,

with a **LifeTool**, basketball.

How do you deal with YOUR:

STRESS

EMOTIONS,

PROBLEMS?

UNLESS *we are* managing our stress, emotions, life problems & issues *they will be managing us!*

Just as isolation **FUELS** the illness
So too does our **stress**, our **emotions** & **life issues**.

Healthy coping skills minimize the impact!

When it comes to **LifeTools**
Here are some

Transformation Tips!

To stay where you are:

✓ **HOLD** everything inside

✓ *Keep using* your old "Survival Tools"!

- ✓ Continue to *BLAME* everyone else for your problems.

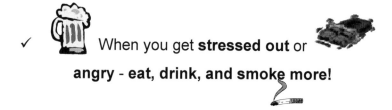

- ✓ When you get **stressed out** or **angry - eat, drink, and smoke more!**

- ✓ Refuse to see how your survival tools may be hurting you

- ✓ AVOID dealing with things.

- ✓ **Don't change.**

Most important to getting well!

1. Take **100%** responsibility for your actions and emotions.

2. Be **open** to trying NEW *ways of coping.*

3. *Instead of* avoiding things-DEAL with them!

4. Try talking or writing about how you feel.

5. Take a at what's working & **what's not.**

6. Replace old survival tools with new Lifetools.

7. Break BIG problems and issues down in to **small piles**.

8. Be willing to & do ask for help.

9. Let the tears FLOW!

Day 10 – Communication

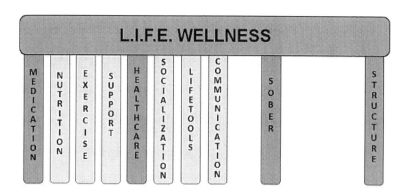

If I could teach only one skill to people, this is it!

Let's face it – it's nearly impossible to just get through a day **without** communicating!

I believe the *QUALITY* of life is greatly influenced by the *QUALITY* of our communication skills.

Most important is our ability to *EXPRESS our needs* and emotions.

(No one can know what they are until we say them!)

There are **3** basic approaches in communication:

Aggressive

Assertive

Passive

Aggressive: My needs and wants are all that matters! It is my way or no way.

Passive: My needs and wants aren't important at all. I'll just keep them to myself

Assertive: My needs and wants are just as important as your needs and wants are.

WAIT!

I forgot the 4th one!!

Passive-aggressive

This is the **MOST** *DAMAGING*

to our relationships

Because it can leave us feeling they're

NOT BEING honest with us.

Behaviors speak louder than words!

Examples:

1) Rather than *tell the waitress* the service was poor –

I don't leave a tip!

2) When you ask "What's wrong?" -

I say **"nothing"**

Yet, you can tell by my tone & body language

"*something*" is!

3) Instead of me *telling you I am angry*,

I slam doors & drawers, make a lot of noise,

or purposely do things to annoy you!

4) I communicate by **what I don't say**!

the silent treatment, showing up late,

or not calling when I'm supposed to!

It's like someone trying to SNEAK IN to your home

through the **BACK**

rather than walk in thru the front

There's another way I like to have people think about it:

Imagine we are both sitting at the table.

We are sitting face to face across from one another.

How would *you prefer* to be 'served'?

- I **shove** everything at you!

- I **set it** on the table in front of you so you can take what you want.

- I **don't put anything** on the table, leaving you with nothing at all.

or

- I set it in front of you then **take it away**, pretending it was never there in the first place!

 Think about it...

How do you 'serve' other people?!

Do you need to do any work on your **communication skills?**

It is also possible that you are a combination of different styles!

Maybe in certain situations you can be passive

While in other situations you can be **assertive!**

I used to be passive aggressive at home

And yet assertive at work!

When it comes to **Communication**

Here are some

Transformation Tips!

To stay where you are:

✓ Believe that people *should know what you are thinking?*

✓ *Hold* everything in & don't speak up.

✓ **Refuse** to see the need to ~~CHANGE~~

✓ Continue to be ***passive aggressive***

& HURT your relationships

✓ Keep doing what you've been doing.

✓ Believe that if *he/she loved me…*

they wouldn't have to ask.

✓ Let your **emotions** come either
roaring out or sneak out in subtle ways.

Most important to moving forward!

1. Recognize that *no one knows what you are thinking* until you **tell them**.

2. Be willing to '*put things on the table*', not shove them at someone.

3. **Stop** holding *everything inside.*

4. If you can't express yourself verbally,

 try writing instead.

5. Work on *improving* your communication skills.

6. *Don't* let **emotions** build up!

Day 11 – Spirituality

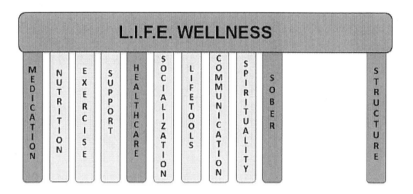

L.I.F.E. WELLNESS

MEDICATION | NUTRITION | EXERCISE | SUPPORT | HEALTHCARE | SOCIALIZATION | LIFE TOOLS | COMMUNICATION | SPIRITUALITY | SOBER | STRUCTURE

The *most important thing* when it comes to spirituality:

It is up to us, *as individuals,*

how we will define this.

Years ago, I had a person offer a wonderful definition.

It's the one I use to this very day!

"*Spirituality is the way or ways in which we create an inner sense of peace.*"

For some people this is religious services.

For others it may be prayer, meditation,

readings, or listening to recordings.

Do you have any spiritual practices?

Did you have them & STOP then

as your illness got worse?

Maybe you feel like this area does not apply to you.

I can respect that.

You simply move on to the next day in the foundation.

Most important to getting well!

1. Listen to some music that may connect for you.

2. Do some reading, even if it is just a quote.

3. Make a point to do some small step everyday.

4. Try to attend services a shorter period of time.

5. Engage in conversations about your spirituality.

Day 12 – Leisure

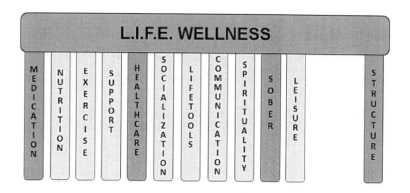

One of the things I've noticed is that when symptoms start to get worse people's leisure interests/activities stop.

Leisure plays a very important role in wellness for several reasons:

1   It can often be what we use to create structure in our free time.

2   It helps feed so many of our values & needs.

3   It can act as a balancing force in our lives:

      Example: Work and play

                      Indoors and outside

                      Activity and inactivity

What are some of the things you **used to like to do**?

How did you **used to feel doing them**?

When it comes to **Leisure**

Here are some

Transformation Tips!

To stay where you are:

✓ **Wait** to do things again until you 'feel' like it.

✓ Spend all your free time either in bed

    o or watching

✓ When you're feeling BORED –

✓ **Stay indoors**! *Do not* step outside at all!

✓ Remain **Unwilling** to try new things

✓ Turn down **ALL invitations** to do something.

Most important to getting well!

1. **Start SMALL!** *Every little thing counts!*

2. ***DO THEM!*** *Even if you don't feel like it!*

3. *Push yourself* to start doing leisure activities again.

4. **Limit the amount** of time you sleep and watch TV

5. Step outside!
   Even if it's just for 2 minutes.

6. **Get active!**

Do something *requires you move.*

7. **DON'T EXPECT** to pick up where you left off.

8. Be **p a t i e n t** with yourself!

9. **Dig out** the interests that

   got buried in the illness!

Day 13 – Acceptance

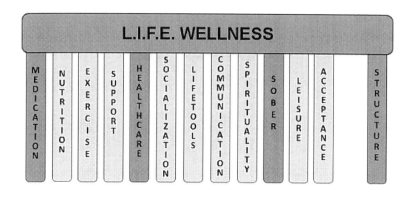

L.I.F.E. WELLNESS

MEDICATION | NUTRITION | EXERCISE | SUPPORT | HEALTHCARE | SOCIALIZATION | LIFETOOLS | COMMUNICATION | SPIRITUALITY | SOBER | LEISURE | ACCEPTANCE | STRUCTURE

I may be able to convince you to follow the

L.I.F.E. Wellness Blueprint™ for a short while -

Yet, if you're going to continue this wellness journey

for any longer period of time..

(for me it's *the rest of my life* &

I hope the same for you!)

the key is

Acceptance

Let's be clear…

acceptance *does not mean* **LIKE!**

I haven't meant anyone who *LIKES* being ill!!

acceptance means

recognizing the illness is *part of our lives*

&

we need to learn how to live with it as a part of our life.

My experiences have taught me

we all don't reach this place

of acceptance *the same way!*

For some people,

it might **be easier** than **for others.**

What's important is that we recognize reaching

the place of acceptance is a PROCESS

One way I'd have my patients monitor this

is using this scale:

0%   100%

Where would you put your level

of acceptance on this scale?

Use this monitor your progress!

The important question I have to ask you is this:
Is what you are *doing* in your life *WORKING?*

If it **IS** – great!   Don't change a thing!

If it **ISN'T** – how about *making some changes!*

Here's my wordtool for accept

A
Conscious
Choice
Enabling
Powerful
Transformation

Here's my wordtool for acceptance:

A

Conscious

Choice

Enabling

People

To

Acknowledge

New

Circumstances

Exist!

When it comes to **Acceptance**

Here are some

Transformation Tips!

To stay where you are:

✓ Keep asking yourself "**Why me**?"

✓ Continue to play the *'blame game'*

✓ Hold on to the attitude it's not fair

✓ See things aren't working but <u>don't change.</u>

✓ **Ignore** warning signs of illness

✓ Believe you are *the only one* with this issue.

Most important to moving forward!

1. 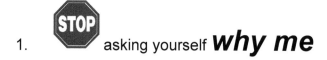 asking yourself **why me**

2. Understand an *illness is* **NOT WEAKNESS**

3. Recognize how *BLAMING* will keep you stuck.

4. Remember:

   It's not *what happens to us* but

   what we **DO** about it!

5. Be *open & willing* to change what is not working.

6. **Get involved** with a support group – you aren't the only one.

7. Continue to work towards acceptance.

8. Realize you are able to have **WELLNESS** at the same time you have an illness!

Day 14 – Self Esteem

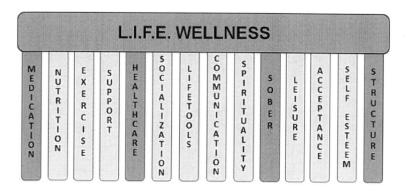

Last but not least – *self-esteem!*

The simple definition I use for self esteem

"How we *feel about ourselves*"

Something I've noticed with self-esteem & illness:
There are 2 groups people seem to fit in to.

In the 1st group are the people
who had good self-esteem until they got sick.

It went downhill from there.

The **2nd** group of people are different.

Self-esteem didn't go down when they got sick -
they *didn't have very much to begin with.*

The bad news here is it will take a *little more work*.

I like to get people thinking of building self esteem
as being like growing flowers...

It all starts with planting 'seeds'!

From there
it requires 'care and feeding' in order to grow!

Some people were *fortunate* -

They *had seeds planted*
when they were young.

Others were *not so fortunate*…

We can't go back and change the past…

we can only take care of **today**

It is **never too late** to start planting!

Another way I like to get people to THINK about
self-esteem is as a tree!

When a storm hits – what happens?
Branches break off!

Trees with a **strong root system** –
Can weather the STORM!!

When self-esteem is based
on things *outside* of you:

home, job, children, money, roles, etc.…

It can all be taken away in a STORM!

When self-esteem is based
on things *INSIDE* of you:

values, qualities, characteristics,
WHO you are – not what you are.

These are the "roots" that STAY LASTING!

When it comes to **Self-Esteem**
Here are some

Transformation Tips!

To stay stuck where you are:

✓ Continue to **see ourselves as a victim** of a bad childhood (if it applies).

✓ Engage in **negative** and critical self-talk.

✓ Let *other people's opinions* of you - become **HOW YOU SEE YOURSELF**

✓ BLAME other people for *the way you feel.*

✓ Remain the biggest bully to yourself.

✓ STAY in a toxic and unhealthy relationship.

✓ **ALLOW** people to be abusive to you.

✓ *Let others* make decisions FOR YOU.

✓ Base your self-esteem on outside things like a job, income, role, & possessions,

Most important to moving forward!

1. Do some type of **self-care** activity every day.

2. Take **100%** responsibility for your feelings.

3. Stay **focused** on **today** & catch yourself when you start to dwell on the past.

4. Replace ▬ and critical self-talk with
✚ and supportive self-talk. (Great Job!)

5.  *Start to make*
your own decisions.

6. Recognize what's happened in the past
does not make you a **victim** today.

7. ☠ Stay away from toxic people.

8. **Set limits** and say **"No"**

9. *Do not allow* your **illness** to
define WHO you are!

" THINK BIG "

Remember

1. Plant the seeds!

2. Water daily!

Here's my wordtool for blame:

Become

Lost

Amongst

Many

Excuses

Other Ways to use the Blueprint

There are **2** other ways to use

the L.I.F.E. Wellness Blueprint™:

We use it to build a **ladder** so we can

"**climb out of that big black hole**" we've been in....

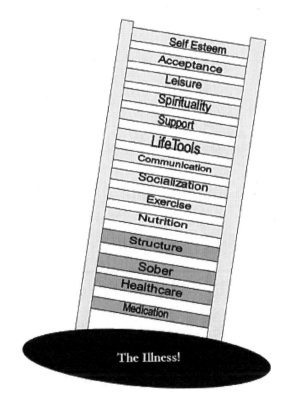

Or we use it to build a **cage**

so we can keep that beast of an illness

from running loose in our lives:

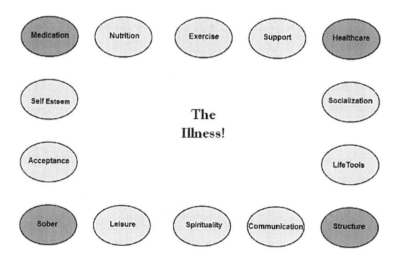

If medication is *not* a part of your life

please use the following amended blueprints!

No medications

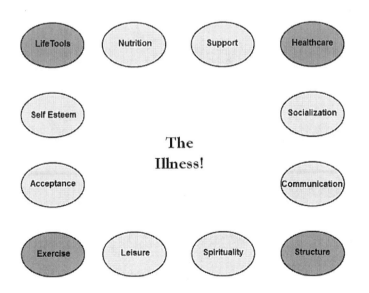

No medications

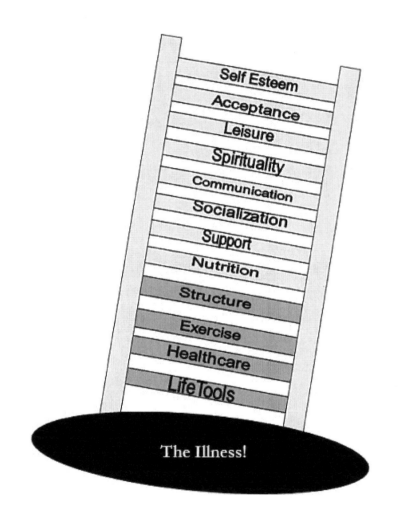

Tools

For Change

Changeology!

Over the past **23** years I've developed some great tools for making lasting change.

Did you know there are actually ways we can set ourselves up TO FAIL – *before we even start?*

Will power is one of those ways!

It *might* help us make *short lived change* –

However, **it doesn't** help us very much when we are trying to make **LASTING** change.

Willpower is like a battery! You can only use it for so long before it starts to weaken!

On to

Tools for CHANGE!

Tool # 1

*Focus on what you will **GAIN!***

Not on what you'll lose.

This is usually the **1st** place where people get it wrong. They actually do the opposite!

"If I don't quit smoking, I could die"

"If I don't lose this weight, the doctor says I could have a heart attack or a stroke"

"I don't want to get fired so I better learn this new computer program"

Instead:

*"If I quit smoking, **I'll be able to walk Carol down the aisle at her wedding**!"*

*"I want to be 40 pounds lighter **so I can play ball with my grandson.**"*

*"By learning this new program, I am **making myself more qualified for a better job!**"*

Tool # 2

START **SMALL!**

This is usually the **2nd** place people get it wrong!
Again, they tend to do the opposite!

Whatever the change is –

Break it down in to **baby steps 1**st

Exercise:

Start by walking during commercials.

Then go out for a 5 minute walk.

Slowly build up the time to 20-30 min.

If for some reason you

DON'T *FEEL LIKE* doing it –

Make yourself **do just 1 min** & then **STOP!**

This way it continues **to build the momentum**

and won't slow your progress.

Tool # 3

Use an *anchor!*

Write the change you are making

on a small piece of paper or an index card.

It should be written in the following way:

In the *present tense,*

using only *positive language,*

& with *feeling attached!*

Examples:

" I am so happy being able to
walk Carol down the aisle!"

"I feel grateful I can now play ball with my grandson."

I am excited with having new job opportunities!"

Read it:

✓ **Wake up**

✓ **Before sleep**

This will help keep you "anchored" to the healthy changes you are In the process of making!

Here's my wordtool for change:

C reating

H ealthy

A nd

N ew

G rowth

E xperiences

Tool # 4

CHANGE *is* *a process!*

It is something we aim at – like a target
but don't beat ourselves up if we miss!

Remember, learning anything *new* requires

practice for it to become a **NEW** habit.

This is WHY change is a process!!

Don't get discouraged when you find yourself
slipping back to old behaviors.
Learn from the 'slips' and move on.

2 steps forward, **1** step back
still has us *moving* CLOSER to **our goals.**

Try this exercise!

START on one side of a room.

Take TWO STEPS forward

&

ONE STEP **back.**

Now, do it again!

Take TWO STEPS forward

&

ONE STEP **back.**

Repeat this process at least *2 more times!*

Are you closer to the other side
of the room than where you started?

So when your *brain* starts to YELL at you:

'you're going backwards'

Yell back! "No I'm not!!"

Here is my wordtool for: Practice

Purposely

Repeat

Activities

Critical

To

Improving

Core

Existence

Here is my wordtool for: Failure

Find

An

Important

Lesson

Using

Real

Experiences

Wrapping Things Up

We started off by looking at how

deciding & doing are *2 different things!*

Congratulations on getting to this point.

WE MUST NOW DO: *Direct opportunity!*

Then we took a (👓) at a definition of wellness

&

identified how illness & wellness can

CO-EXIST!

Yet, there is no wellness possible without taking:

1st responsibility for putting it in place

2nd action to make it present in our lives.

ACTION:

A Critical Task Implemented Only *NOW!*

Next,

you learned about the blueprint for

It is **critical** to get those corners in place

& *KEEP* them in place!

Medication

Healthcare F/U

Sober

Structure

Without them – we DON'T stand a chance!

I *encourage* you to not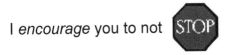

At just the **4** corners...

REMEMBER:

The more legs the better!

STABLE

SOLID

STURDY

STRONG

 can cause EVERYTHING to come crashing down!

We've got to make sure we **have enough**

so if we lose some of our foundation

We've still got plenty to

&

keep wellness in our life!

138

Putting It All Together!

Start with Day 1 & keep adding on the days.
Before you know it – you'll have a foundation in place!

Remember -

when it comes to putting things in place

it all comes down to "Baby Steps"!

By taking 'small actions' every day
we are building that foundation a little bit at a time!

Brick by brick! Day by Day!

A BONUS TOOL!

We have a special
bonus for you!

Go to:

www.WellYOUniversity.com/MeasuringTape

Put your name and email in the box

Click "Send Me My Measuring Tape Carol!"

Once you have confirmed it is okay to add you

to our email server, we will send you an email.

The email will contain an assessment you can use to

measure the strength of your wellness foundation

& identify areas to focus on!

Be on the lookout -

It will come from Well YOUniversity!

About the Author

Carol Rickard, LCSW, TTS has written over a dozen publications & conducted national training workshops on stress and wellness.

She is the founder and CEO of Well YOUniversity, LLC, a global leader in health education & training, whose mission is to empower individuals with the tools and supports to achieve lifelong wellness.

Carol is a popular speaker / trainer at all types of conferences and events. She provides community education for hospitals, continuing education programs, staff professional development and CEU/CME courses.

Her high energy, unique approach and compelling presentation change thinking and inspire participants to take action towards L.I.F.E wellness (Living Intentionally & Fully Engaged).

Carol can be reached at Carol@WellYOUniversity.com.

Facebook: www.FaceBook.com/WellYOUniversity

Please visit us at:

www.WellYOUniversity.com

Sign up for weekly motivational e-quote!

Check out our upcoming FREE webinars!

Learn more about our training programs.

Email us your success story at:

Success@WellYOUniversity.com